CW00409447

THE TOP TEN LOVE SONGS TO PLAY ON PIANO

WISE PUBLICATIONS
part of The Music Sales Group
London / New York / Paris / Sydney / Copenhagen / Berlin / Madrid / Hong Kong / Tokyo

Published by
Wise Publications
14-15 Berners Street,
London W1T 3LJ, UK.

Exclusive Distributors:
Music Sales Limited
Distribution Centre, Newmarket Road,
Bury St Edmunds, Suffolk IP33 3YB, UK.
Music Sales Corporation
180 Madison Avenue, 24th Floor,
New York NY 10016, USA.
Music Sales Pty Limited
Level 4, Lisgar House,
30-32 Carrington Street,
Sydney, NSW 2000 Australia.

Order No. AM1012275
ISBN 978-1-78558-402-2

Compiled by Naomi Cook.
Notes written by Greg Johnson.

Photos courtesy of:
Page 5: House Of Fame LLC/Michael Ochs Archive/Getty Images
Page 11: Michael Ochs Archives/Getty Images
Page 18: Michael Putland/Getty Images
Page 24: Dick Barnatt/Redferns
Page 29: Richard E. Aaron/Redferns
Page 33: Paul Bergen/Redferns
Page 41: Sascha Steinbach/Getty Images
Page 46: Michael Tran/FilmMagic
Page 53: Julie Clarke/WireImage
Page 59: Lynn Goldsmith/Corbis/VCG via Getty Images

Printed in the EU.

Your Guarantee of Quality
As publishers, we strive to produce every book to the
highest commercial standards.
This book has been carefully designed to minimise awkward
page turns and to make playing from it a real pleasure.
Particular care has been given to specifying acid-free, neutral-sized paper
made from pulps which have not been elemental chlorine bleached.
This pulp is from farmed sustainable forests and was
produced with special regard for the environment.
Throughout, the printing and binding have been planned to
ensure a sturdy, attractive publication which should give years of enjoyment.
If your copy fails to meet our high standards,
please inform us and we will gladly replace it.

www.musicsales.com

THE TOP TEN LOVE SONGS TO PLAY ON PIANO

Something about the indescribable nature of love has had songwriters constantly churning out songs on the topic for centuries. Perhaps it is the unique marriage of words and music that somehow fulfils the purpose of expressing what is seemingly impossible to say. Whatever the reason, there is a wealth of romantic songs out there that cover every aspect of love, but which ones really hit the spot? Well, that's where we come in...

This carefully-compiled collection features some of the most heartfelt, heart-breaking and uplifting tracks ever committed to record by artists who knew how to describe the dramas, the tragedies and, of course, the delights of love. From Etta James to Adele, Elton John to Evanescence and Roberta Flack to the Bee Gees, prepare yourself for an emotional rollercoaster.

AT LAST

ARTIST: Etta James
RELEASED: 1960

Originally written for the 1942 film musical *Orchestra Wives* by Mack Gordon and Harry Warren, 'At Last' was the signature song of famed jazz and soul singer, Etta James. She released the song as a single in 1960 and, although it only achieved modest success in the mainstream Billboard 100 charts, it peaked at No. 2 in the R&B listings, and has only grown in popularity as the decades have drawn on, as well as being covered by many other artists.

The track was already regarded as a standard by the time James came to perform and record it, but it was her version, with instrumentation by the great Chicago-based arranger Riley Hampton, that became the definitive interpretation of this romantic classic. Less schmaltzy than many other great love songs, 'At Last' is a more sultry number, somehow grounded despite the almost giddy lyrics. James may have believed the track to be hers and hers alone, but in truth it now belongs to the world.

AT LAST

Words by Mack Gordon
Music by Harry Warren

and here___ we are___ in hea-ven,

for___ you are mine___ at___ last.___

colla voce

a tempo

mf

CLOSE TO YOU
(THEY LONG TO BE)

ARTIST: The Carpenters
RELEASED: 1970

It may have been the breakthrough hit that made brother-sister duo The Carpenters household names, but 'Close To You (They Long To Be)' was a song that had a life before Karen and Richard Carpenter were offered the chance to record it. Written by Burt Bacharach and Hal David, it was first released by Richard Chamberlain in 1963 but failed to find its audience. Later that same year, Dionne Warwick recorded her version, released in 1964 as an album track and B-side. Bacharach himself even released it as a single in 1968, but

it was The Carpenters who turned the song into a Grammy-winning, worldwide smash hit in 1970. Their version was so successful and well-loved that the song and the group have since become all but inseparable.

The piano features heavily in the band's arrangement, with that famous opening introducing the use of suspensions that characterises the accompaniment throughout the song and reinforces the sense of yearning described in the lyrics.

CLOSE TO YOU
(THEY LONG TO BE)

Words by Hal David
Music by Burt Bacharach

(EVERYTHING I DO)
I DO IT FOR YOU

ARTIST: Bryan Adams
RELEASED: 1991

A No. 1 hit in 18 countries, '(Everything I Do) I Do It For You' is one of the most successful single releases of all time. It holds the record for an amazing 16 consecutive weeks spent at the No. 1 spot – a number that is unlikely to be matched now that we generally consume music in a different way. The song was written and recorded in London back in 1990 by Bryan Adams, Michael Kamen and Robert Lange, who also produced the track. In 1991 it was released on two albums simultaneously: Adams' sixth studio album, *Waking Up The Neighbours*, and the official soundtrack to *Robin Hood: Prince Of Thieves*.

Despite being performed by an artist who is more often associated with guitar-led songs (as the studio album cover confirms), '(Everything I Do) I Do It For You' features the piano. But this is no delicate, touch-feely love letter. Bryan Adams (and Robin Hood for that matter) don't have time for that. This is a song about passion, risking it all for romance and doing whatever it takes to be with the one you love.

(EVERYTHING I DO)
I DO IT FOR YOU

Words by Bryan Adams & Robert John Lange
Music by Michael Kamen

1. Look in-to my eyes, you will see,
2. Look in-to your heart, you will find there's

what you mean to me. Search your heart, search your
noth-ing there to hide. Take me as I am, take my

THE FIRST TIME EVER
I SAW YOUR FACE

ARTIST: Roberta Flack
RELEASED: 1972

When Ewan MacColl first penned this love song for Peggy Seegar, who would later become his wife, he apparently taught his lover the tune down the phone and sent her tape recordings to listen to while they were apart. They would go on to perform the song together as a duo in folk clubs across the UK. Eventually, the song was picked up and covered by other artists on the scene and beyond, including Elvis Presley, who recorded and released his own version of the song.

It wasn't until Roberta Flack put her spin on the track that it became a popular hit. At almost half the speed of the original, it was a very different interpretation that captured the imagination of the public and important figures in other creative fields. Clint Eastwood chose Flack's version to be used in his directorial debut, *Play Misty For Me*, while as a single it sat at the top of Billboard Hot 100 for six consecutive weeks. It is a touching, heart-rending piece of music when placed in the hands of Flack, with the piano underscoring her emotive vocals with a quiet, discreet beauty all of its own.

THE FIRST TIME EVER I SAW YOUR FACE

Words & Music by Ewan MacColl

1. The first time ev - er I
2. The first time ev - er I
3. The first time ev - er I

saw your face,
kissed your mouth,
lay with you

I thought the sun
I felt the earth
and felt your heart

and the end-less skies.
at my com-mand, my love.

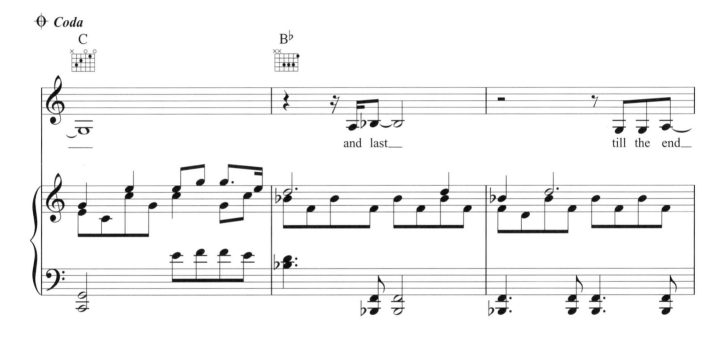

and last___ till the end___

___ of time,___ my love.___ The first time___

HOW DEEP IS YOUR LOVE

ARTIST: Bee Gees
RELEASED: 1977

The first of six consecutive No. 1 hits in the USA for the Bee Gees, 'How Deep Is Your Love' was featured on the soundtrack to the 1977 film *Saturday Night Fever*, released in the same year. Work first began on the track in demo form in 1976 in a French Château just outside Paris before continuing on back in Miami, where the group were based during the period. After reaching the top spot in five other countries, and peaking at No. 3 in the

UK charts, the song was nominated for two Grammy awards, winning the Bee Gees the gong for Best Pop Performance by a Group in 1978.

This is a lovely piece for pianists. Filled with harmonic interest and played at an easy, relaxed tempo, it has that feel-good factor that will keep you coming back again and again.

HOW DEEP IS YOUR LOVE

Words & Music by Barry Gibb, Maurice Gibb & Robin Gibb

I WILL ALWAYS LOVE YOU

ARTIST: Whitney Houston
RELEASED: 1992

Dolly Parton wrote and recorded 'I Will Always Love You' in 1973 as a valediction to her former partner after she decided to pursue a solo career. She became the first artist to score two No. 1 records with the same song after releasing the track as a single on two separate occasions. But, of course, that's not the end of the story...

In 1992, Whitney Houston recorded her version of the song for the film *The Bodyguard* and it became one of the best-selling singles of all time, spending 14 weeks at No. 1 in the USA and topping charts around the world. After her death in 2012, Houston's version of the song charted again, reaching No. 3 in the Billboard charts – another landmark for this record-breaking track which became only the second single ever to reach the top three in separate chart runs.

With a soft, almost bell-like synth tone, the keys in the track not only complement the other musical elements but help to bring out the nuances in Houston's performance, punctuating her meandering expressions before later providing even greater emphasis to her powerful projections. It is a veritable tor de force of a love song.

I WILL ALWAYS LOVE YOU

Words and Music by Dolly Parton

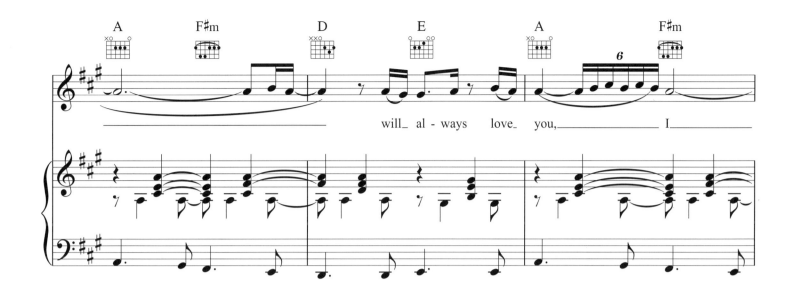

will_ al - ways love_ you,_____ I_____

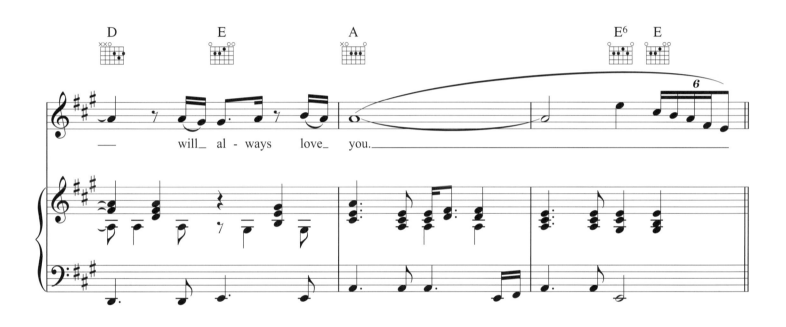

— will_ al - ways love_ you._____

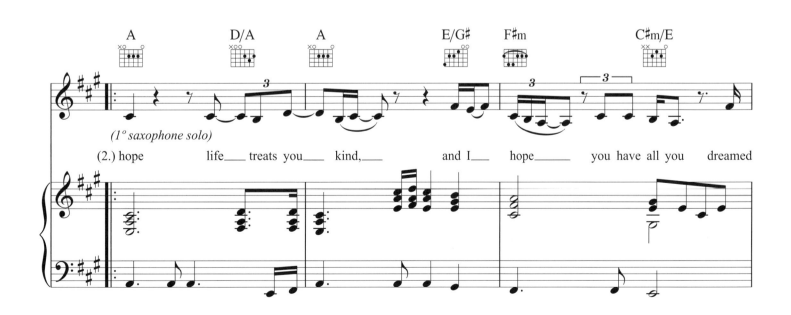

(1° saxophone solo)

(2.) hope life____ treats you____ kind,____ and I____ hope_____ you have all you dreamed

of._____ And I wish you joy_ and_ hap-pi - ness:_____ but, a-bove all_

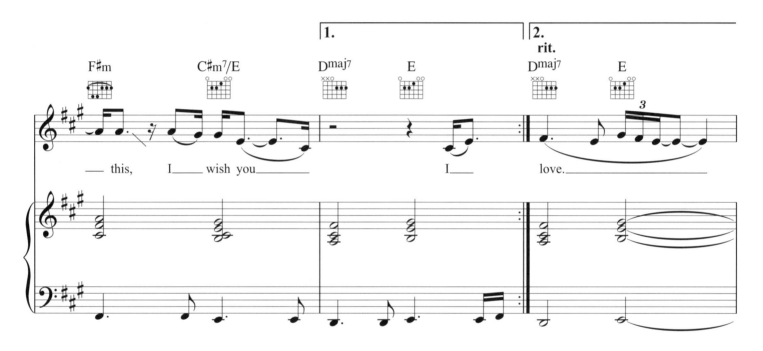

_ this, I_ wish you_____ I_ love._____

And I_____ will al - ways_ love_

you,_____ **6**_____ I will al - ways_____ love_ you,_____ I_____ will al -

- ways_ love_____ you,_____ **3** I, I will al - ways_ love you,_

_____ I will al - ways love____ you,_____

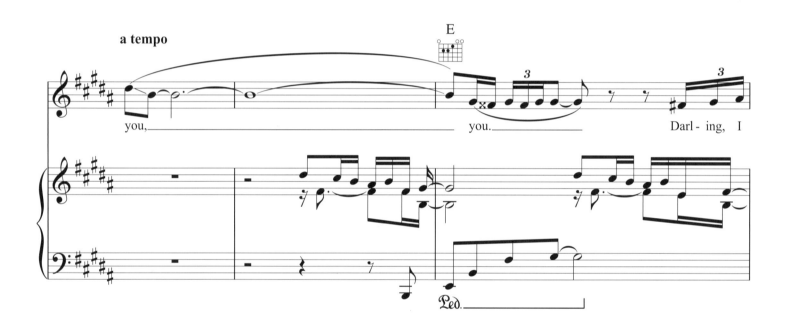

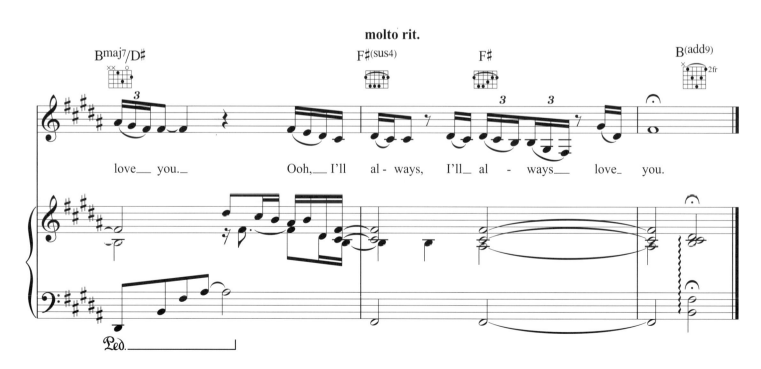

MAKE YOU FEEL MY LOVE

ARTIST: Adele
RELEASED: 2008

Despite writing the song for his 1997 album *Time Out Of Mind*, Bob Dylan was not the first artist to release 'Make You Feel My Love'. He was beaten to the punch by Billy Joel, who put out his version as a single earlier that same year. The song went on to be covered by numerous other artists, most notably by Adele, who included it on her debut album, 19, in 2008. It was released as the fifth and final single from the album and initially peaked at No. 26 in the UK charts, only to shoot back up the listings two years later to eventually reach No. 4 after a performance on the TV talent show *The X-Factor*.

This song is a brilliant example of the beauty that can be found in simplicity; the delightful balance of voice and piano that sits at the heart of Adele's cover and the uncomplicated melodic phrases perfectly complement the simple message: I would do anything for you.

MAKE YOU FEEL MY LOVE

Words & Music by Bob Dylan

1. When the rain is blow-ing in your face, and the whole world is on
2. When the eve-ning shad-ows and the stars ap-pear, and there is no one there to dry

to make you feel my love.____

MY HEART WILL GO ON
FROM *TITANIC*

ARTIST: Céline Dion
RELEASED: 1997

A hugely successful smash hit that will forever be associated with the 1997 film *Titanic* – itself a record-breaker at the box office and one of the highest-grossing motion pictures of all-time – 'My Heart Will Go On' was the movie's main musical theme, performed by French-Canadian singer, Céline Dion.

Also known as 'Love Theme From Titanic', it was written by composer James Horner, whose other credits include *Braveheart* and *Avatar*, with lyrics by multi-award-winning songwriter Will Jennings. However, it was Dion's powerful and emotional performance

that helped convince director James Cameron that it should be included in the film. The version that featured on the soundtrack and was released as a single was in fact the original demo of the song which had orchestral parts added at a later date.

This is a bruising titan of a love song that translates to piano really well, thanks to the arpeggiated figures that recur throughout. It demands a heartfelt performance so try to inject lots of expression into your playing.

MY HEART WILL GO ON

FROM *TITANIC*

Words by Will Jennings
Music by James Horner

MY IMMORTAL

ARTIST: Evanescence
RELEASED: 2003

A top ten hit in 16 countries, including the USA, UK and Germany, 'My Immortal' was the third single from Evanescence's debut album, *Fallen*, and the fourth song written for the group following their formation in 1995. It was originally meant to appear on an early, self-released EP in 1997 but it was cut from the track list and would later be reworked and recorded into a number of different versions prior to becoming a major hit in 2003. The final version actually features the vocals of singer and co-writer Amy Lee from the original demo version with new instrumentation written by Ben Moody to build upon the piano arrangement by the band's former keyboard player, David Hodges.

The ballad came as something of a surprise to casual listeners of the band, who had come to expect the band's single releases to be in-keeping with the nu-metal sounds of their earlier hit, 'Bring Me to Life'. Its popularity soon spread beyond the limits of the early 00's metal scene and the song became a staple of weddings, engagements, anniversaries and many other romantic proposals and passionate gestures. No 21st century list of the best, most beloved piano love songs would be complete without it.

MY IMMORTAL

Words & Music by Ben Moody, Amy Lee & David Hodges

YOUR SONG

ARTIST: Elton John
RELEASED: 1970

Certified as platinum in the USA, 'Your Song' was a top ten hit for Elton John on both sides of the Atlantic in 1970 but was originally released as a B-side to 'Take Me To The Pilot'. Radio play saw to it that the track gained popularity in its own right. The song itself was written by John and his long-time writing partner Bernie Taupin, who provided the lyrics. He wrote the words on the roof of the publishing company building that John worked at prior to his success – more than just a bit of trivia, the location is even referenced on the track.

An ideal conclusion to this collection, this classic piano ballad not only showcases some of the best writing of the genre but the lyrical content brings us back to considering the reasons so many artists write love songs – in this case, the protagonist describes all the things he would buy his lover had he enough money, but concludes that what he can give is the very song he is writing: it's a message to his partner; the song allows him to 'put down in words' just how he feels.

YOUR SONG

Words & Music by Elton John & Bernie Taupin

1. It's a lit-tle bit fun-ny,_____ this feel-ing in-side._____
2. If I was a sculp-tor,_____ but then a-gain, no,_____ or a
(Verses 3 & 4 see block lyrics)

I'm not one of those who_ can ea-si-ly hide.
man_____ who makes po-tions in_____ the tra-vel-ling show.___

you're_ in____ the world._____

Verse 3:
I sat on the roof and kicked off the moss.
Well, a few of the verses, well, they've got me quite cross,
But the sun's been quite kind while I wrote this song;
It's for the people like you that keep it turned on.

Verse 4:
So excuse me forgetting, but these things I do;
You see I've forgotten if they're green or they're blue.
Anyway, the thing is, what I really mean;
Yours are the sweetest eyes I've ever seen.

And you can tell everybody *etc.*